**"To all the children who have lost a brother or sister,**
**and to all the children and grown-ups who help them cope!"**
Avichai Hoter

Terrorism is something children cannot understand. Most adults cannot understand it either. The hate that makes it possible to kill people for no other reason than their being Jewish - how can anyone begin to grasp such depths of inhumanity?
Avichai's story is the story of all Israelis. It is so hard for us to understand why we have lost so many. And the fear lingers – constantly there – that others will be taken from us. We try to maintain our normal lives, find happiness, and rediscover hope. We try, in vain, to heal ourselves and make life the same as before.
**OneFamily** helps give hope and happiness to those who have been hurt by terrorism – the wounded, those who have lost their heroes. And since life can never be exactly as it was, **OneFamily** will continue to be there to help – and to hope.

Thank you for being a hero to thousands of victims of terrorism.
You are now their brother or sister.
Because we are all **OneFamily**.

Marc Belzberg,
Chairman, OneFamily Fund

# My brother was ...

**Elaine Hoter PhD**

Clay Sculpture: Jonathan Bereskin
Illustrations and Graphics: Nadia Adina Rose
Clay Photography: Noam Huber

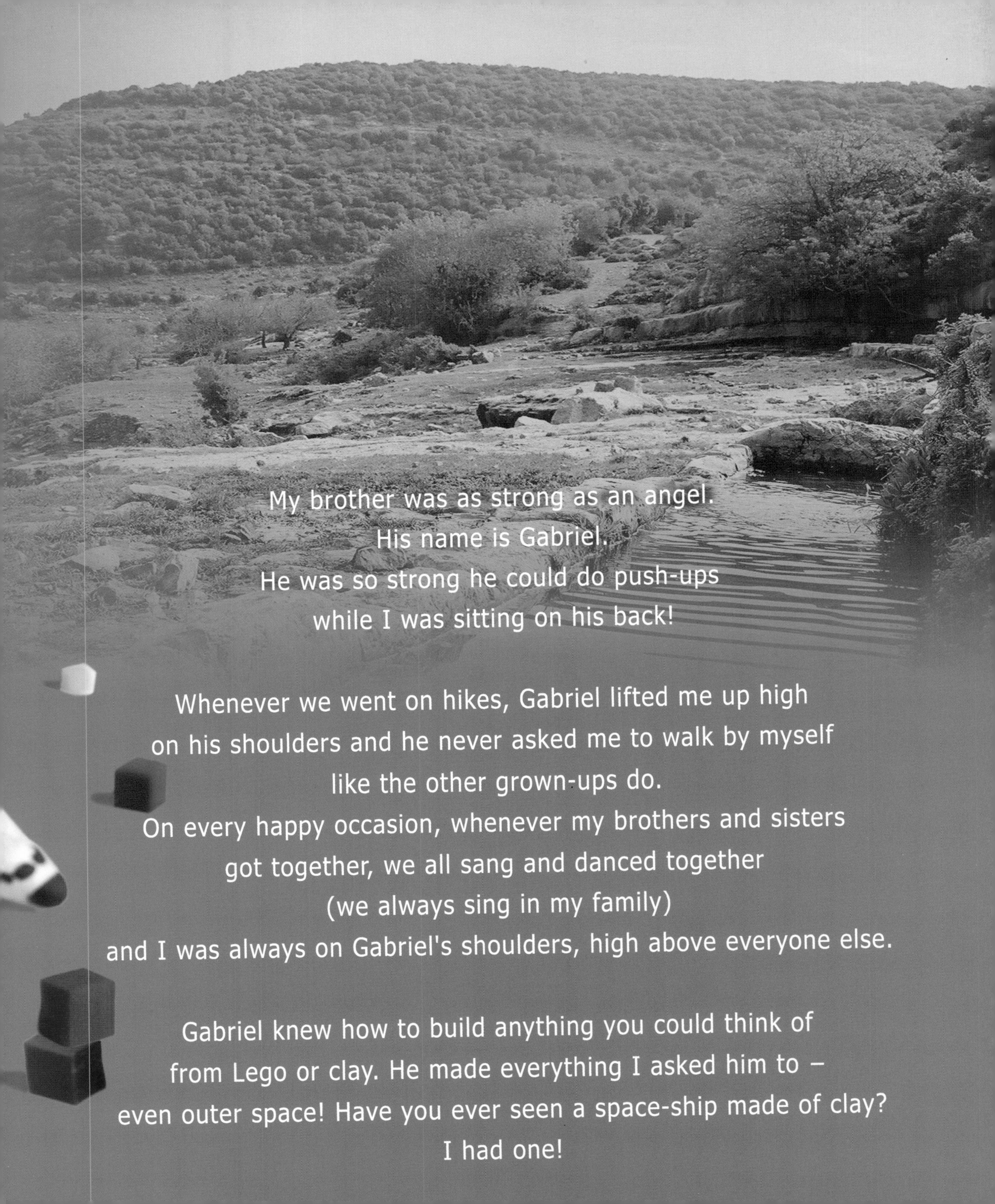

My brother was as strong as an angel.
His name is Gabriel.
He was so strong he could do push-ups
while I was sitting on his back!

Whenever we went on hikes, Gabriel lifted me up high
on his shoulders and he never asked me to walk by myself
like the other grown-ups do.
On every happy occasion, whenever my brothers and sisters
got together, we all sang and danced together
(we always sing in my family)
and I was always on Gabriel's shoulders, high above everyone else.

Gabriel knew how to build anything you could think of
from Lego or clay. He made everything I asked him to –
even outer space! Have you ever seen a space-ship made of clay?
I had one!

And suddenly on Saturday morning there was a knock on the door.
They told us that Gabriel had been murdered in a terrorist attack.
I started laughing,
I thought it was a joke!
Gabriel was so strong – how could anyone hurt him?
Yes. I thought it could only be a joke.
But it wasn't.

We went to the funeral.

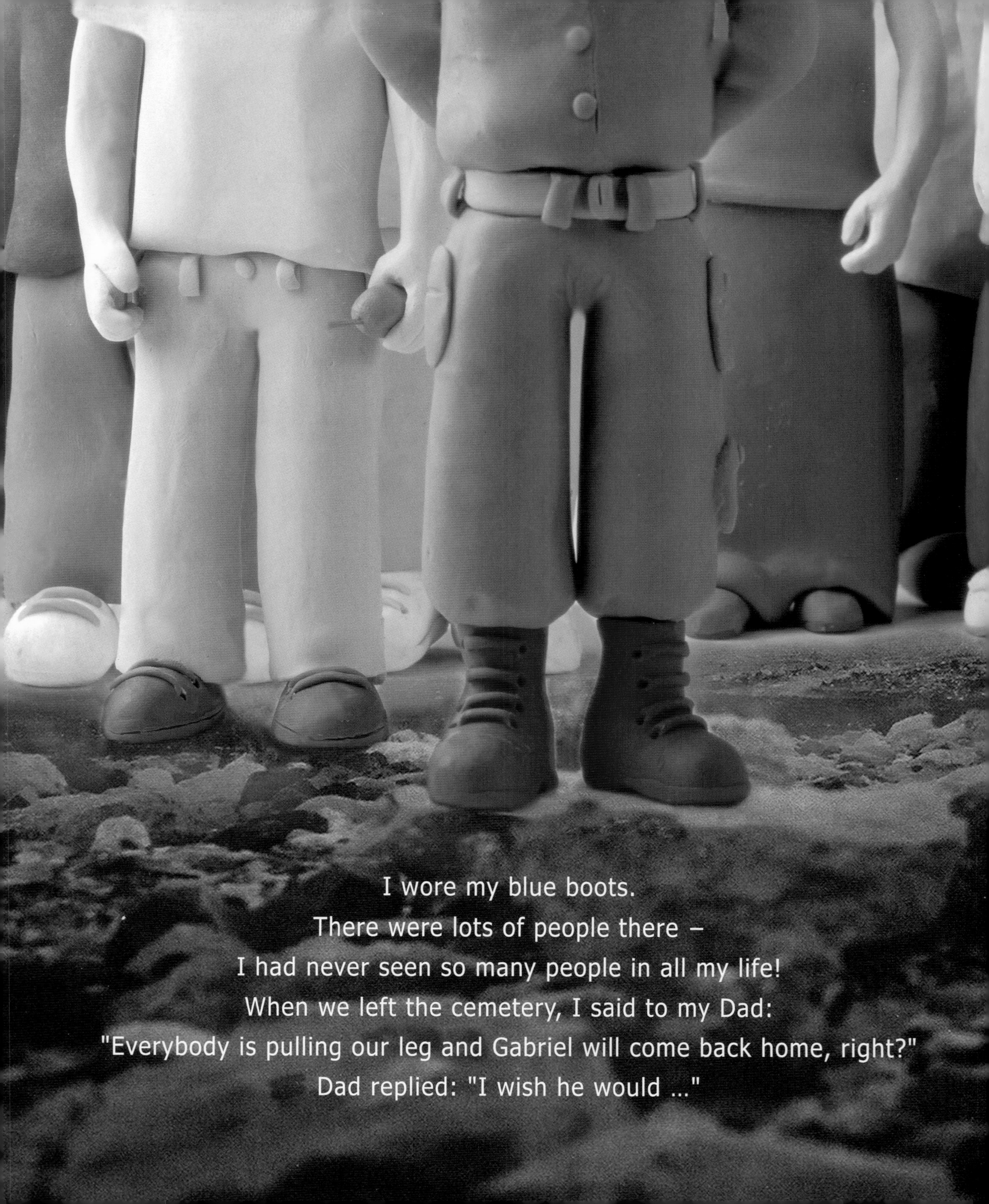

I wore my blue boots.
There were lots of people there –
I had never seen so many people in all my life!
When we left the cemetery, I said to my Dad:
"Everybody is pulling our leg and Gabriel will come back home, right?"
Dad replied: "I wish he would ..."

Everyone was so sad.
And I wanted everyone to be happy again.
I said to my Mom:
"Now you can call me Gabriel."
I thought that way everyone would be happy again.
Mom said to me: "No way – you are our cute Avichai.
We don't have any other Avichai.
I love you because you are Avichai, our child,
and we don't want you to be anybody else."

It was nearly Purim.
This is my favorite holiday, when we all get dressed up.
I decided that I wanted to dress up as a terrorist.
I thought that a terrorist is like a cowboy – he always shoots first!
But at home they weren't too excited about the idea.
My family bought me an Israeli soldier paratrooper costume.
I put on my new uniform and I looked like a real soldier,
with my red beret and all the badges and medals.
And then I decided to behave like a brave soldier.

Everyone spoke about my brother.
Everyone told stories about him.
Everyone said that we have to learn from my brother Gabriel.
I tried to think what would be the best thing for me to learn from Gabriel.
I thought so hard all week that I could hardly sleep.

I started to wake up in the middle of the night –
I was really scared.
I was worried about Gabriel.
Maybe he's lonely and doesn't have friends?
Where is he? What's he doing?
Does he have clay there like he had at home?
Maybe he's giving art classes to all the angels?
Perhaps he has Lego and he's making space-ships
and sending them into outer space?
People tell me he's in heaven, but I can't see him anywhere.

One night I had a dream.
I saw my brother Gabriel and asked him:
"Gabriel, why don't you come home?"
I told him how sad everyone is.
Gabriel told me that he can't come home because G-d needs him.
In my dream, Gabriel lifted me up onto his shoulders,
just like he always did,
and we danced and sang together.
After my dream, I stopped worrying about Gabriel.

It was still sad at home. Mom cried a lot.
I don't remember ever seeing my Mom cry, but now she cries a lot.
I said to my Mom: "Every time I see you crying I'll give you a kiss,
and then you have to stop crying right away." And that's what I did.
I know that whenever I give my Mom a kiss, she'll think how lucky
she is to have a cute kid like me, and then she'll stop crying.

We still sing a lot at home, but slower songs,
songs that help us all feel better.
Gabriel's friends taught me a really nice tune to the words
"Even though I walk through the valley of the shadow of death,
I will fear no evil for You are with me."
They also told me that the song has magic powers:
When you sing the song together, you stop feeling scared.
I sing the song all the time and I've even taught it to all of my friends.

One day in kindergarten I played a game with my friends.
We were all sitting in a circle. I was playing an old guitar
and a friend of mine, Dina, was lying down on the floor
and pretending to be my wife who had just died.
My friends and I sang the song with the magic power again
and again and again. And then the Messiah came!
Actually, it was my good friend Ariel,
but in our game he was the Messiah.
We all got up and danced and sang.
Even Dina, who was dead in the game,
came back to life and we danced happily together.

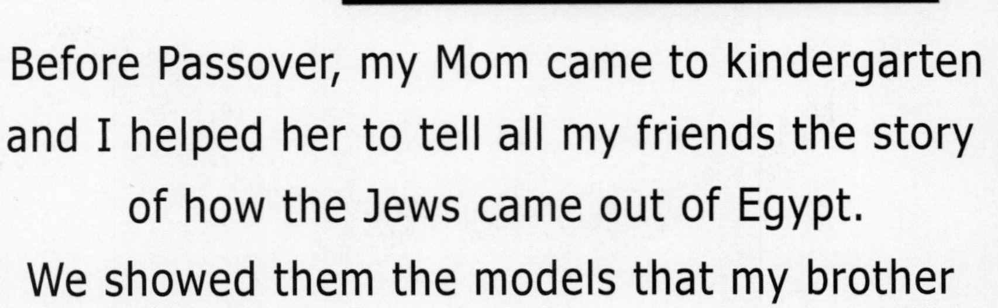

Before Passover, my Mom came to kindergarten
and I helped her to tell all my friends the story
of how the Jews came out of Egypt.
We showed them the models that my brother
made out of clay when he was 11 years old.
All the children loved the figures Gabriel made!
Then we all took different colored clay
and we also made the story of the Jews coming out of Egypt.
Ayala the kindergarten teacher said our work was really beautiful
and she decided to make an exhibition, just like real artists.

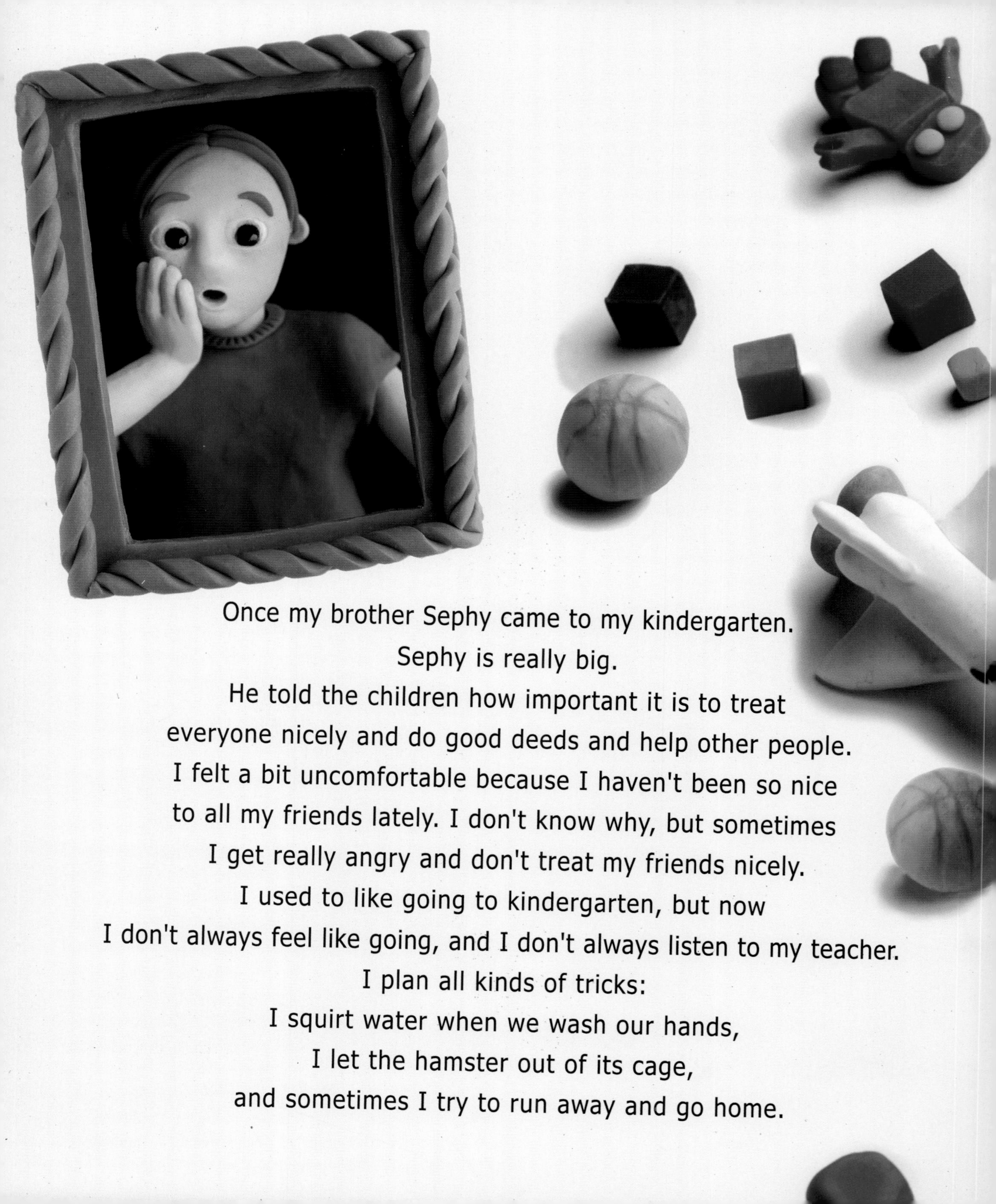

Once my brother Sephy came to my kindergarten.
Sephy is really big.
He told the children how important it is to treat
everyone nicely and do good deeds and help other people.
I felt a bit uncomfortable because I haven't been so nice
to all my friends lately. I don't know why, but sometimes
I get really angry and don't treat my friends nicely.
I used to like going to kindergarten, but now
I don't always feel like going, and I don't always listen to my teacher.
I plan all kinds of tricks:
I squirt water when we wash our hands,
I let the hamster out of its cage,
and sometimes I try to run away and go home.

I started feeling scared at night again.
I woke up crying.
I told Mom my bad dream:
"I was working with Dad, building the new house
like we do almost every day, and suddenly the police came.
They got out of the car and shot my Dad!"

What a scary dream!

I told Mom that I've been thinking a lot lately.
I've been thinking that it's a terrible thing when a brother or sister dies.
But I think it's worse if a mom or dad dies,
because for me, my Mom and Dad are everything.
And then I told my Mom my secret –
why I want to run away from kindergarten:
It's to check up and see if my Mom and Dad are OK.

Mom hugged me very, very tight.
She told me she'd talk with my kindergarten teacher
and ask her to let me call home
when I want to check that everything's OK.
She hugged me again and told me that everyone loves me,
and I don't need to worry because usually only old people die.
But I know that sometimes it doesn't happen that way.

Now we smile and laugh more at home,
especially when the whole family gets together and my
nephews and nieces come over. I got two new nieces in one year.
There is no other uncle in my kindergarten - only me!
Everyone plays around with them and we sing and dance just like before,
well, nearly ...

Background photography: Roi Shefa, z"l; Shimon Biton; Elchanan Zonenfeld

Clay figurines of the Exodus: Gabriel Hoter, hy"d

Translators: Adina and Elaine Hoter

Language editor: Batya Lederfein

Thanks to all those who read the book, commented on it and supported the project:

**Rabbi Neriah and Eva Mansur** who lost their 15 year old son **Aviad** in a terror attack while we were working on the English version of the book;

the Hoter and Hellerman families; Heidi Cherney, z"l, and her daughters;

Roni Oren; Shella Shorshan-Roznak; Zehava Kor; Uri Orbach; Nadine Kaplan;

Michal Fechler; Meira Borenstein; Gita Narinsky; Rabbi Reuven Grodner; Joe Nakash;

Suzie Weiss Ben David; Roy Speiweck, Hava Simon, Dr. Reina Reiner; Rasi Feldman;

Orly Ben Haim; Miriam Turgeman; Iris Zonenfeld; Gila Shneider; Judith Paull Litoff;

Ayala Arzi – the most wonderful, patient and loving kindergarten teacher in the world!

And to everyone else who helped us and was there for us.

This profound and painful book has been written from the viewpoint of a child. We are taken hand-in-hand with him through the stages of his bereavement – from his first difficulties in receiving the painful news, through his simple attempts to "correct" the situation and then onto a time when he can properly deal with it. Here is a child who dreams, plays, fears for his parents, and tries to organise his suddenly destabilized world in a manner that gives it meaning and internal logic. This book does not give simple answers or remedies. But it does provide a focus and resource for parents who want to connect, together with their children, with the internal experience of bereavement.

We at the **OneFamily Youth Division** believe in the inner strength that children possess which enables them not only to deal with bereavement but also to emerge stronger from the experience. We have taken it upon ourselves to give these children unconditional love, understanding and inclusion. We create a place for them where they can grow and express themselves in an atmosphere of trust and happiness.

Yonatan Amit
Psychologist
**OneFamily Youth Division**

**OneFamily is a unique organization providing direct financial, legal and emotional assistance to victims of the recent terrorist attacks in Israel. Our total commitment to respond to the needs of each individual has resulted in the development and sponsorship of a wide range of programs, including: therapeutic retreats; support groups; workshops; holiday events; home and hospital visits; missions abroad; and, of course, financial support. Through our Adopt-A-Family and Bar or Bat Mitzvah twinning-programs we have involved caring and supportive individuals, and even whole communities, from all over the world – this helps ensure that every victim feels that, no matter where we live, we are bonded to each other and are all OneFamily.**

**"Give me the strength to go on,**
**To bind my burning wounds,**
**To know that I won't get to see him again,**
**To continue  in spite of the pain ...**

**To know – that he forgives me for everything,**
**To feel – his warm embrace,**
**And that always, always he will be with me,**
**Gabriel is somewhere in the skies."**

Words: Dafna Heiman & Michal Hoter
From the song: "Wrapped in a Tallit"
from the disc "the Missing Voice"

This book comes with a disc of "the song that stops you from bring afraid"
from the disc "The Missing Voice", performed in Hebrew by the Hoter family.
Words: Psalms XXIII: 4
Melody: Rabbi Shlomo Carlebach
Adaptation and musical production: Jonathan (Adi) Raz'el
Guitar: Dudu Tassa
Piano and keyboard: Jonathan Raz'el
Bass guitar: Naor Carmi
Drums: Avi Avidani
Cello: Doron Toyster
Recorded in Studio #1, Talpiot, Jerusalem

Clay sculpture: Jonathan Bereskin
Landscape photography: Shimon Biton
Graphics: Tirza Zabari and Nadia Adina Rose


04-6960029
Midreshet Gavriel
www.gavriel.org